Fingerlings

friendship @ your fingertips

COLLECTOR'S HANDBOOK

CONTENTS

Rarity rating

x4 – Ultra Rare

x3 – Rare

x2 – Legendary

x1 – Popular

MEET THE FINGERLINGS!

Fingerlings are the friendliest animals you could meet. There are mischievous Monkeys, dreamy Unicorns, s-l-o-w Sloths, gentle Pandas, fiery Dragons, playful Foxes, laid-back Elephants, friendly Dolphins and dazzling Narwhals.

All of them are different, but they have one thing in common – they all believe in togetherness. Every one of them loves their Fingerling friends more than anything else in the world!

The Fingerlings are lucky enough to live in a beautiful place called Melody Village. It has everything they need to fill every day with fun – and with learning experiences, too.

ALIKA

UNICORN

Alika is a magical Unicorn. She can turn raindrops into gumdrops and tears into laughter. All it takes is a sprinkle of her colourful enchanted glitter!

Likes: Glittery things
Dislikes: Anyone who doesn't believe in magic
Beauty tip: Use magic hair gel – it makes your tail grow extra long!

Rarity rating

It's a secret
Nobody knows where Alika keeps her magic sprinkles. Maybe she hides them in her mane!

8

AMELIA
MONKEY

Amelia is one of the Glitter Girls – a group of four singing Monkeys. Wild, free and fearless, Amelia is never afraid to try a new song.

Rarity rating

Favourite food: Cherries – she always tries to get the last one!
Dislikes: Having a sore throat
Best friends: Rose, Kiki and Sugar

Always in tune
The Glitter Girls talk, argue, laugh and even cry in perfect harmony!

9

AQUA

DOLPHIN

Aqua thinks it's funny to splash her friends. She sneaks up in the water, flips her tail, and then... splash! Not everyone finds it as funny as Aqua does!

Rarity rating

Likes: Splashing everyone!

Dislikes: Tangly seaweed that slows you down

Favourite flowers: Dolphiniums

Water good name!
Aqua has the best ever name for a Dolphin. It actually means "water."

10

ARCHIE

PANDA

This sparkly blue-and-white Panda just loves to grab onto things. Once he has made friends with you, he will never let go!

Favourite food: Blueberry pie
Favourite dance: The Panda Polka
Likes: Clinging on tight with all his might!

Gentle Archie
Archie never grabs at butterflies. He knows they are very delicate.

Rarity rating

11

AVA

MONKEY

Ava is a daring two-tone Monkey. If there is a new place to explore or a new food to try, you can trust adventurous Ava to jump right in!

Rarity rating

Cheer up!
If Ava sees anyone looking sad, she tries to cheer them up by making funny faces.

Likes: Anything new
Bad habit: Not looking before she leaps
Favourite drink: Every kind of fruit juice, all mixed together

BEANIE
PANDA

This little panda loves all things soft. She sleeps in a soft, leafy bed. She munches soft foods, such as avocado. She even speaks in a soft voice!

Favourite music: Soft string music... ahhhh!
Dislikes: Hard foods such as nuts... ughhhh!
Pastime: Watching fluffy clouds float by

Rarity rating

Panda pal
Beanie always greets her friends with a big wave – then an even bigger hug!

13

BELLA

MONKEY

Bella is Boris's twin sister. Cheerful Bella enjoys staying fit and loves to help friends out – her to-do list never seems to end!

Ee... ee... ee! That's "hi" in Monkey Latin!

Likes: Healthy food, gymnastics, bubbles
Favourite comic book: *Unicornia*
Hero: Ilsa Jumpanov, the world bouncing champion

Monkey talk
Bella and Boris speak a special language called Monkey Latin.

Rarity rating

14

BLUES

DOLPHIN

Blues loves attention – and he gets it! This daring Dolphin thrills his friends with sky high somersaults and tail-tip balances.

Likes: Hearing his friends cheer and clap him
Dislikes: Belly flops. Ouch!
Party trick: Singing a song while balancing a ball on his nose

Record breaker
When Blues broke the tail balancing record, his mood fin glowed all kinds of happy colours.

BORIS

MONKEY

Boris is a playful Monkey, and a noisy one. He chatters and frolicks all day. He loves rock music and plays the drums – loudly!

Rarity rating

Favourite rock band: The Hoomans
Favourite food: Cereal
Big secret: He has a cuddly toy named Major Monkey!

Boris's favourite joke
How do you catch a Monkey? Climb a tree and act like a banana!

16

CANDI
MONKEY

Candi is this Monkey's name, and candy is her favourite treat! She loves to visit her Unicorn friends in Sparkle Heights. They have all the best candy!

Healthy smile
Sweet-toothed Candi brushes her teeth often to keep them clean and shiny.

Rarity rating

Likes: Sugary toppings
Dislikes: Sour things like lemons (unless they are sherbert lemons!)
Dream day out: A visit to a candy factory

CHARLIE

MONKEY

What's better than a banana? A yummy, creamy banana split! That's what this ice-cream loving Monkey thinks.

Rarity rating

Extra sauce
Charlie always asks for extra sauce on his banana split. He's cheeky like that.

Favourite hangout: The Banana Shack
Best friend: Olly, the server at the Banana Shack
Dislikes: Pickles

DREW

PANDA

Drew's panda colours can make him look a little serious. In fact, the only thing he is serious about is having fun!

Likes: Dancing, singing and just goofing around
Music player: Big bad bamboo boombox
Dislikes: Being mistaken for a skunk!

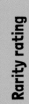

Rarity rating

Party panda
When Drew starts dancing, the party really kicks off. It's panda-monium!

19

EDDIE

MONKEY

Eddie the Monkey is as cool as a cucumber. He looks a little like one, too! He's sleek, green and often seen hanging from a vine.

Rarity rating

Likes: Chilling, chatting and cracking jokes
Dislikes: Fuss and bother and getting all wound up
Motto: It's all good!

Why worry?
Nothing gets Eddie rattled – he's a chilled out, worry-free zone.

20

EMMA

MONKEY

Emma is a two-tone Monkey who lets everyone know her favourite colour. She's pink from her topknot to her toes!

Favourite drink:
Pink lemonade
Favourite fruit:
Pink grapefruit
Favourite bird:
Pink flamingo

Think pink
Emma often dreams of painting the Vines pink. Would her friends like it as much as she would?

Rarity rating

21

FIESTA
MONKEY

Holá, amigos! It's time to party!

Fiesta the Monkey turns any party into a carnival. She dances to the music in her rainbow hat, and always wants to go first at the games.

Conga queen
At one party, Fiesta led the longest conga line in the history of Melody Village.

Likes: Bursting piñatas
Dislikes: Running out of nachos
Favourite party game: Pin the tail on the Monkey

22

FINN

MONKEY

Finn does things his way – the cool way! When everyone else is going ape, this laid-back Monkey just laughs. He would rather be swinging!

Nobody tells *me* what to do!

Likes: Gigi calling him "Finn-dude-o!"

Dislikes: A fuss about nothing

Hairstyling product: Silky Simian Serum

Speech! Speech!
At Sydney's birthday party, Finn gave a speech so long that everyone fell asleep!

Rarity rating

23

GEMMA
UNICORN

Gemma is a Unicorn with a sparkling sense of humour. When she's telling jokes, she always has a twinkle in her eye.

I bring sparkle to every day!

Gemma's favourite joke
What street do Unicorns live on? Mane Street!

Favourite drink: Cherry-flavoured soda
Favourite accessory: Gemstone hooflets
Likes: Making her friends laugh and smile

Rarity rating

GIGI

UNICORN

Gigi's life is a whirlwind of fun! She wants her "fam" (her friends) to join in, but her nonstop prancing and chatter can leave them feeling dizzy!

Likes: Rainbows, hearts, sweets and glitter
Home: A crystal mansion
Favourite music: Electronic dance-pop

Selfie star
Gigi loves to include friends in her selfies – as long as she is at the front!

Rarity rating

GRAY
ELEPHANT

Gray is all about peace, love and harmony. This happy hippie elephant is a mellow dude with a chilled-out mood.

Likes: Enjoying Mother Nature
Favourite smell: Flowery incense
Pastime: Playing soft, trumpet sounds

Rarity rating

Flower power
Gray loves flowers. Mostly he just watches them grow. If he is feeling energetic, he might make a flower chain.

26

JOJO
UNICORN

This Unicorn is always in the pink! Jojo has a glittery pink coat, hot pink hooves and a peach mane and tail. Only one thing isn't pink – her fabulous emerald horn.

I'm absolutely tickled pink!

Rarity rating

Favourite treat: Peaches and cream
Likes: Brightening everyone's day
Motto: Everything's just peachy!

27

JULES

DOLPHIN

This perky pink Dolphin is the entertainer of the oceans! Her funny tricks include surfing air waves and walking on her tail – backwards!

Here we go!
When Jules is about to perform a trick, she winks her eyes and wiggles her tail.

Motto: All the sea's a stage!
Likes: Giving big, salty kisses!
Dislikes: Rough seas – they send her into a tailspin!

Rarity rating

KAYLA

FOX

This friendly fox is not shy. Or maybe it just doesn't show when she is blushing. She's one of the pinkest Fingerlings there is!

Rarity rating

Foxy fiction
Kayla loves a good comic book. She likes to imagine she is the hero of the tale.

Likes: Brushing and styling her bushy tail
Favourite dance: The foxtrot
Favourite flowers: Pink foxgloves

KAYLIN

DRAGON

When Kaylin visits Melody Village, she always brings the heat. This little dragon loves to chill, but she can be fiery when she gets cross.

Rarity rating

Likes: Flying high in a summer sky
Favourite treat: Ice cream... with chilli sauce
Favourite smell: Bacon frying

Pretty fly!
Kaylin's hot pink wings sparkle and shine as she flies.

KIKI

MONKEY

If you ask for Kiki's opinion, you will get the truth. She is very blunt! When she sings, however, this Glitter Girl could not sound softer or sweeter.

Motto: Tell it like it is!
Favourite flowers: Lavender and violets
Worst argument: When Amelia took the last cherry on the plate

Talking in music
The Glitter Girls can speak a musical language that nobody else understands.

Rarity rating

31

KINGSLEY
SLOTH

Kingsley is a lazy, laid-back Sloth with a silly sense of humour. He hangs out all day at Sloth Beach, just soaking up the sun.

Likes: Just hanging!
Dislikes: Being asked to hurry up
Favourite food: Leaf tacos, leaf slaw... leaf anything!

Surf's up! When riding rad waves, Kingsley is anything but slow.

Rarity rating

LEXI

DRAGON

Lexi has fiery breath and a fiery temper. Just stubbing a toe is enough to make this Dragon snap. When she does – look out!

Rarity rating

Likes: Firework displays – big, loud, noisy, colourful ones
Favourite colour: Hot pink
Favourite flower: Snapdragon

Cool it!
Lexi always says sorry after losing her temper. She just needs time to cool down first!

LIBERTY

MONKEY

Her name is Liberty, but unlike the statue, this Monkey is never still. She hops and bops all day in a dazzle of red, white and blue.

Likes: Fireworks, noise and razzle-dazzle
Dislikes: Being shushed!
Ambition: To dance in a marching band

Star-spangled
Liberty's colours are just like those on the flag of the USA – only glittery!

34

LIL' G
GIRAFFE

Lil' G is tall, blue and walks with a strut. He's super-cool, but super-friendly too. Everyone loves this cheerful Giraffe.

Too cool for Boris
Boris used to feel "dorky" compared to the cool Giraffe. Now the two are friends.

Rarity rating

Likes: Feeling the cool breeze in his hair
Dislikes: Bumping his head on low branches
Favourite clothing: A black leather jacket

35

LUNA

DRAGON

Luna shines like the moon, but she has no dark side. This sweet Dragon would fly to the moon and back for her friends.

Rarity rating

Likes: Flying in the moonlight
Favourite flying move: Luna's loop-the-loop
Favourite treat: A big, round, white, frosted cookie

Perfect name
Luna's name means "moon" in Latin – the language of the ancient Romans.

36

MACKENZIE
UNICORN

Mackenzie lights up everyone's life! This happy Unicorn is the proud owner of a very special horn – it glows and changes colour!

Favourite jelly bean:
Coconut flavour
Motto:
You glow, girl!
Favourite colour: Blue... or pink... or yellow... or maybe green...

Full of beans
Mackenzie goes crazy for jelly beans. Boris locks up his supply when she is around.

Rarity rating

MARGE
SLOTH

Marge is a very smart Sloth. She loves reading about the wonderful world around her. She loves exploring it even more!

Likes: Bugs, clouds and treasure hunts
Collects: Books, maps and telescopes
Hidden talent: Freestyle rapping (to slow beats)

It's been a hard day of exploring. Zzzzzz...

Musical Marge
Marge enjoys loud techno music. She dances to it in her room every night!

Rarity rating

MEADOW
GIRAFFE

Meadow is like a model – tall, cool and chic. She's no diva, though. All this pink Giraffe wants is to share laughs with her friends.

I always stick my neck out for my friends!

Rarity rating

Funny feet!
Finn joked that Giraffes have long necks because their feet smell. Meadow secretly found it funny!

Likes: The heart pattern on her head
Dislikes: Scarves that are not long enough
Favourite food: Leaf Stroganoff

MELODY
SLOTH

Melody is a special Sloth. She's the only one who glitters! Her cool moves and super-slow grooves really sparkle under disco lights.

Rarity rating

Likes: Dancing the night away at Disco Slow
Favourite food: Anything except fast food
Nail polish: She won't tell!

Tip-top toes
Does Melody paint her toenails, or is that bright pink colour natural? Who knows!

MELON

MONKEY

Melon is a Monkey who loves fruit. When he's snoozing, he dreams of grapes and lychees – and big green and pink watermelons!

Favourite day out: A picnic with friends

Dislikes: Litterbugs – especially those who drop fruit peels

Motto: Eat more fruit!

Two colours
Colourful Melon is one of the two-tone group of Monkeys.

Rarity rating

41

MIA

MONKEY

Mia is curious about the big, wide world, and about her friends, too. This inquisitive Monkey asks so many questions that she often runs out of breath.

Likes: Learning new things every day
Dislikes: Not having an answer to a question
Favourite words: Why? What? Who? When?

Monkey memory
Once Mia has learned a fact, she never forgets it. She's a Monkey memory bank!

Rarity rating

MIKEY
FOX

Mikey the Fox loves to play pranks. His den is filled with tricks and props. He likes to dance, too – if no one is watching!

Favourite music: Classical string music
Likes: Getting primped at the foxtail salon
Catchphrase: "I didn't do it!"

Perfect prank!
Mikey's favourite prank is gluing a coin to the floor and watching his friends try to pick it up.

Rarity rating
🐾🐾🐾🐾

43

MOLLY
UNICORN

Molly is a restless Unicorn. When she is excited, her voice gets really squeaky. This giddy Fingerling can make even Gigi look calm!

Working out
To stay fit, Molly goes to Gigi's Twirlates class. The Lollipop Lunge is her favourite move.

Best moment:
Appearing on Gigi's "Unicorny" game show
Favourite colour:
Rose gold
Exercise:
Twirlates class

Rarity rating

NELLY

NARWHAL

Nelly the Narwhal lives in the sea. If she spots a friend on the shore, she leaps out of the water flipping her tail. It's her way of waving to them!

Likes: Exploring coral reefs
Ambition: To get her Unicorn friends to come for a swim!
Dream: To find a treasure chest

Song of the sea
As Nelly swims along, she trills a sweet and happy Narwhal song.

Rarity rating

NIKKI

NARWHAL

Nikki's light-up horn changes colour with her mood. When she's having her head tickled, it glows bright green!

Have a hug!
Nikki has very strong flippers. She gives really great hugs!

Hobby: Synchronized swimming with her Narwhal friends
Motto: Make a splash!
Favourite song: Hey Nikki

Rarity rating

46

NINA

ELEPHANT

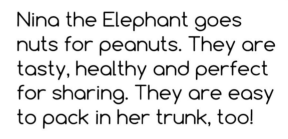

Nina the Elephant goes nuts for peanuts. They are tasty, healthy and perfect for sharing. They are easy to pack in her trunk, too!

Rarity rating

Favourite snack:
Peanut cookies
Favourite music:
Jazz trumpet
Pastime: Shell art using peanut shells

Nina's favourite joke
Did you hear the joke about the peanut butter? I'm not telling you – you might spread it!

47

NOA
DRAGON

Noa is a fierce little Dragon – fierce about being loyal! She sticks by her pals, and quickly takes anyone new under her sparkly wing.

I never let a friendship go cold!

Likes: Warm hugs... really warm hugs!
Dislikes: Seeing a friend unhappy
Favourite pastime: A campfire sing-along

Hold fire
Noa tries not to burn anything with her breath!

Rarity rating

48

NORI

NARWHAL

Nori is named after the salty seaweed she loves to nibble on. This on-the-go Narwhal needs a lot of energy for her ocean acrobatics!

Like a Unicorn
Narwhals are known as "Unicorns of the sea" because of their horns. Nori thinks that's fun!

Rarity rating

Favourite food:
Seaweed s'mores
Likes: Surfing the waves with the Sloths
Favourite saying:
Cowabunga!

49

PARTY
MONKEY

Party is the perfect name for this fun-loving Monkey. He won't leave the dance floor, and if anyone turns off the music he goes ape!

I'm a real party animal!

Favourite dance: The Funky Monkey
Dislikes: Going home!
Favourite sounds: Loud music and party poppers

Hat trick
If you see Party putting on his shiny gold hat, you know where he's going.

Rarity rating

50

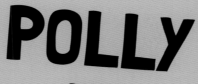

POLLY

PANDA

Polly the singing Panda needs regular naps. When she's snoozing, her friends just roll her along. She'll wake up in her own sweet time!

Likes: Singing, drawing, painting and slumber parties... zzzzzzzzzz!

Dislikes: Alarm clocks

Best moment: Singing on stage at the FingMu club

Don't talk – sing!
Polly doesn't speak. When she wants to let someone know how she's feeling, she sings it.

Rarity rating

51

QUINCY

MONKEY

Quincy glitters blue-green, like the sea. He is never seasick though, even when he spins upside down in the trees!

Likes: Hanging by his tail and spinning – fast
Dislikes: Being mistaken for a bird
Favourite dance: The Monkey Macarena

I'm sea green and I'll give you a wave!

Bright boy
Quincy is the first glitter boy, and the first green glitter Monkey.

Rarity rating

RACHEL

NARWHAL

This popular pink Narwhal is always floating between her friends. She lets them know she loves them by giving them a big kiss!

Likes: Bumping into friends unexpectedly
Dislikes: Being on her own
Motto: Toot your own horn!

Kiss Kiss
Rachel loves giving her friends kisses. When she does, she makes loud smoochy noises. Mwaah!

Rarity rating

RAYA

NARWHAL

Raya loves to party! When music plays, she starts dancing and her horn flashes bright colours. She can turn anywhere into a disco!

Likes: Deep-sea dancing with her Dolphin friends
Party trick: Glowing in the dark
Favourite colour: All of them! She just can't make up her mind

Snooze time
When she needs a nap, Raya slips into a nice, comfy bed of seaweed.

Rarity rating

RAZZ

MONKEY

This little Monkey is raspberry red. That's why she's called Razz! She sparkles like a ruby as she swings from vine to vine.

Favourite food: Anything raspberry flavoured
Dislikes: Wet weather
Favourite song: Twinkle, Twinkle, Little Razz

Blue top
Razz's topknot is the same colour as her friend Boris's fur.

Rarity rating

ROSE
MONKEY

Rose is known as "the shy one" of the Glitter Girls. When she sings, however, she shines just as brightly as her three braver friends.

Favourite flowers: Pink, scented roses
Dislikes: Hearing her friends argue
Best friends: Kiki, Sugar and Amelia

Modest Monkey
If anyone praises Rose, she gets bashful. She even hides behind the sofa sometimes!

Rarity rating

56

RUBY
DRAGON

I feel lucky to have my lovely friends.

Ruby is a real gem. This precious little Dragon has a very special power. She brings good luck wherever she goes!

Rarity rating

Golden girl
Ruby's wings and ears glitter like pure gold.

Favourite song: I Should Be So Lucky
Dislikes: Cold weather
Party trick: Using her fiery breath to toast marshmallows

57

SANDY

DRAGON

Sandy is a real hothead! This daring Dragon rarely thinks before she acts, which can get her into all sorts of mischief!

Likes: Surprises of all kinds
Dislikes: Too much talk and too little action!
Motto: What could possibly go wrong?

What's that?
If something catches Sandy's attention, she just has to go and investigate.

Rarity rating

58

SARAH

FOX

Sarah is a perky purple Fox. She's kind and funny, but a little sly. She always seems to pop up when someone has treats or news to share!

Big ears
If anything fun is going on, Sarah soon hears about it. Her big, purple ears are always twitching.

Rarity rating

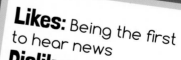

Likes: Being the first to hear news
Dislikes: Being the last to hear news
Favourite song: Purple Rain

SKYE

UNICORN

Skye loves the high life! This flying Unicorn soars through the air, counting clouds or racing birds. She once nearly caught a rainbow!

Hobby: Chasing rainbows
Beauty tip: Always air-dry your mane
Likes: Air dancing with birds, bees and butterflies

No wings
Unlike her Dragon friends, Skye does not need wings to fly. She uses Unicorn magic!

SOPHIE

MONKEY

Sophie is the cuddliest Monkey ever. She says hello with a hug, and goodbye with a hug. Anyone feeling sad gets an extra big hug!

Hey... do you want a hug?

Favourite toys: Soft, squeezy cuddly toys
Likes: Making her friends feel really wanted
Motto: Hug it out!

Rarity rating

It's okay
If a friend upsets Sophie, she soon forgives them – with a hug!

STELLA

UNICORN

Stella is a dreamy blue Unicorn. She believes that if you wish on a shooting star, your wish will come true – lots of hers have!

Favourite wish: To see more shooting stars!

Likes: Nighttime

Favourite rhyme: I wish I may, I wish I might, see a shooting star tonight

Seeing stars
One night, Stella saw so many shooting stars she ran out of things to wish for.

Rarity rating

62

SUGAR

MONKEY

Sugar is a real cry-Monkey! If something makes her sad, happy or angry, her reaction is the same. She bursts into tears!

Rarity rating

Likes: Fluffy tissues and soft handkerchiefs
Dislikes: Seeing others unhappy
Best Friends: Glitter Girls Kiki, Rose and Razz

It's catching
When Sugar starts crying, it often sets off the other three Glitter Girls!

63

SUMMER

MONKEY

Sunshine makes Summer the Monkey very happy. It's so warm and golden! She never turns down a chance to catch some rays.

Rarity rating

Likes: Soaking up the sunshine
Dislikes: Winter – but spring and autumn can be okay
Sunbathing tip: Don't forget your sun hat!

Just beachy
An invitation to Sloth Beach in July is Summer's idea of heaven.

64

SYDNEY

MONKEY

Sydney is a simian singer who makes the Vines echo with sweet Monkey music. Her talent is really off the scale!

Likes: Singing while swinging
Favourite birds: Songbirds – sometimes she duets with them
Favourite music: Swing

Musical styles
Sydney can sing anything, from soul to opera. She's even had a try at yodeling!

Rarity rating

65

TARA

DRAGON

Tara is a daredevil Dragon princess who always speaks her mind. She's full of fiery energy, and doesn't like apologising.

They say I'm hot stuff. That's cool!

Rarity rating

Best moment: Completing her Dragon Quest

Hidden talent: Claw painting

Home: Dragon Palace on Blaze Mountain

Hot topics
Quieter Fingerlings (especially Gray) find Tara and her opinions a little too hot to handle.

TIFFANY

MONKEY

Tiffany is the Fingerlings fashionista. She loves to twirl and pose in the Vines, swishing her tutu. This stylish Monkey is more chic than cheeky!

Rarity rating

Likes: Dressing up
Worst moment: Spilling cherry juice on her favourite dress
Motto: Make that branch your runway!

What to wear?
Tiffany has three garments to choose from – a tutu, a onesie and purple shorts.

67

TUX
PENGUIN

Party trick: Copying his friends in silly voices
Dislikes: Calm seas – big waves are the best!
Favourite song: Surfin' Bird

Perky Penguin Tux chatters on, and on and on. There's one way to shut him up – just ask for a peck on the cheek!

Some birds squawk... I just talk!

Rarity rating

Flying Penguin!
Tux feels like he is flying when he rides a wave on his surfboard.

ZOE
MONKEY

Zoe the Monkey loves life upside down. She sleeps, reads comics, eats lunch and even does her hair while hanging by her tail!

Friend to all
Zoe loves getting to know all kinds of creatures – not just other Fingerlings.

Favourite exercise: Tail pull-ups
Bad habit: Waking up her friends to play
Dislikes: Getting her topknot in a tangle

Rarity rating

MEET THE PAIRS AND GROUPS!

In Melody Village, everyone is a friend. That doesn't mean a Fingerling can't have a best buddy or two. Everyone knows that some groups or pairs are simply inseparable. Anyone who wants a game with one of them will have to take them all on!

Many friend pairs consist of one full-size Fingerling and one Mini. That leads to lots of fun games. The Mini can hang off the other Fingerling. Sometimes they can be swung and caught, too. It's all good fun, and of course, perfectly safe. No Fingerling would ever play rough with their Mini friend.

ALLEC

PANTHER

You won't miss Allec in the dark – or her cute cub, Ronni. This Panther pair have fur covered in silver glitter!

RONNI PANTHER CUB

Rarity rating

Likes: Grooming her beautiful black fur
Dislikes: Spilling milk on her fur
Favourite music: Cat's chorus

Lucky black cat
Ronni is the luckiest black cat of all. She has the coolest, most fun mum ever!

71

ASHLEY

MONKEY

CHANCE MINI MONKEY

Ashley met her little Monkey friend by chance. The two bumped into each other while chasing the same butterfly!

Tree dweller
The name Ashley means "someone who lives near an Ash tree."

Likes: Chasing things
Favourite treat: Tutti-frutti ice cream
Favourite music: Ashley mashup feat. cheeky Chance

Rarity rating

BENNY

TIGER

Benny the Tiger is a purr-fect papa. He loves to play tag with his cub, Kali. Benny usually lets Kali win – by a whisker!

Tiger light
Kali isn't afraid of the dark. Benny's light up fur lets her know he is always close by.

Likes: Snuggling up for a catnap
Dislikes: Being cold
Favourite prank: Hiding in long grass and jumping out. Surprise!

KALI TIGER CUB

Rarity rating

BILLIE

MONKEY

Mini mischief
Aiden can be very naughty. Often, he won't come down from the treetop at bedtime.

Billie likes to give his mini friend, Aiden, a boost. He uses his tail to lift Aiden to the top of the tree. That's where the best bananas grow!

AIDEN MINI MONKEY

Favourite snack: Banana sandwich
Dislikes: Having his tail pulled
Favourite colours: Blue and green

Rarity rating

DANNY
MONKEY

Life is sweet for Danny and her bestie, Gianna. The monkey friends are both covered in bright, candy-coloured stripes.

GIANNA
MINI MONKEY

Rarity rating

Favourite party game: Musical branches
Likes: Boiled sweets in fruity flavours
Dislikes: Boiled cabbage

Cutie spot
Like all mini best friends, Gianna has a cutie mark on her rear.

75

JESS

MONKEY

Jess and her mini Monkey friend, Eden, just won't be parted. They even hook their tails together as they play.

Likes: Linking tails and swinging upside down
Dislikes: When Eden hides as a prank
Best friend: Eden, of course!

EDEN
MINI MONKEY

Rarity rating

RAINBOW
TIGER

Rainbow is a cat of many colours. Just look at her stripes! Her baby, Beau, is turning out to be a colourful cub, too.

BEAU TIGER CUB

Likes: Sunshine after rain
Dislikes: The colour grey. It isn't bright enough!
Dream: To find a pot of gold at the end of her tail

Baby colours
Beau has just started growing stripes. He's still waiting for the green ones!

Rarity rating

77

SAM

LION

Sam loves a joke. She is always roaring with laughter. This friendly Lion is happy that her cub, Leo, is following in her playful pawsteps.

I'm the comedy queen of the jungle!

LEO
LION CUB

Favourite food:
Cubmarine sandwich
Tip: Always keep your den tidy!
Grooming product:
Magical mane mousse

Mane attraction
Sam tells Leo that if he eats his crusts, he will grow up to have a curly mane.

TILLY
TIGER

Tilly the Tiger is teaching Tammy, her cub, to count. How many pink stripes does Tilly have? One, two, three...

TAMMY TIGER CUB

Favourite flowers: Pink tiger lilies – of course!
Favourite game: Tail wrestling
Motto: Glow for it!

Lovely lullabies Tammy likes to drift off to sleep while Tilly purrs her a lullaby.

Rarity rating

79

VIOLET

MONKEY

Violet has named her little buddy Hope. That's because she hopes they will be best Monkey friends forever and ever!

Flower girls
The purple pals both love flowers. They spend hours making flower crowns together.

HOPE MINI MONKEY

Favourite sweets:
Grape wine gums
Likes: Flowers – especially scented purple ones
Best Friend: Hope

FANTASY PACK

DRAGON AND UNICORNS

Bubbles and Becca are a fun-loving duo. They are always giggling, and they both love thinking up ways to amuse their little pal, Bianca.

Two-tone trio
Bubbles, Becca and Bianca are the same colours, but in different combinations.

BECCA UNICORN

BIANCA MINI UNICORN

BUBBLES DRAGON

Fantastic friends
Bianca thinks having a Unicorn *and* a Dragon as best buddies is simply fantastic!

Rarity rating

FINGERBLINGS
MONKEY

Glimmer, Glitz, Glam and Sparkle are a dazzling bunch! These four fabulous Monkeys are known as the Fingerblings. They just love to stick twinkling rhinestones all over their faces.

Having a ball
The Fingerblings love dancing under disco lights. They always try to outglitter the glitter ball.

SPARKLE

GLIMMER

GLAM

GLITZ

Likes: Grabbing attention on the dance floor
Dislikes: Blending into the crowd
Motto: Keep shining!

Rarity rating

HOLIDAY PACK

MONKEYS

Holly loves festive fun with her friends, Jolly and Merri. She likes to hang from the tree, and pretend her tail is a candy cane, which makes them all laugh.

Rarity rating

HOLLY MONKEY

JOLLY MONKEY

MERRI MINI MONKEY

Glittering gift
Last year, Jolly gave Merri a big, glittery gift box filled with banana toffee.

MEET THE PLAYSETS!

Fingerlings are all about friendship, and friendship is all about sharing. No wonder the Fingerlings love to get together and share their playsets with their friends.

Swings, roundabouts, see-saws, jungle gyms, monkey bars – there's something to play on around every corner in Melody Village. There's room for everyone, and everyone is welcome. For the Fingerlings, any time is playtime!

FERRIS WHEEL

PLAYSET

MANDY MONKEY

MEL MINI UNICORN

Who's afraid of heights? Not Mandy and her mini Unicorn friend, Mel. They ride the ferris wheel without a care in the world.

In a spin
A wheel of spinning teacups makes a fun – but dizzy – ride!

JUNGLE GYM
PLAYSET

AIMEE MONKEY

The Jungle Gym has lots of bars to scamper and swing on. Aimee is happy playing alone, but it's more fun when her friends are there!

How many?
Sometimes, Aimee and her friends play "How many Fingerlings can fit on a Jungle Gym?"

MONKEY BARS
PLAYSET

Liv and Simona love to monkey around on the Monkey Bars! They can climb the ladder, hang from the bars or ride in the yellow swing.

NAIMA MONKEY

Fair friends
The Monkey pals always play fair. They are careful to take equal turns on the swing.

SIMONA MONKEY

LIV MONKEY

SLOTH BARS

PLAYSET

The Monkeys aren't the only ones that enjoy climbing. The Sloths also love to play on their very own Sloth Bars!

I could hang here alllll day.

CLARA SLOTH

Lazy days
The Sloth Bars are lots of fun, but playtime is tiring! Luckily, the bars are a great spot for a nap.

SEE-SAW
PLAYSET

Twin Monkeys Milly and Willy are exactly the same size. That means a smooth ride on the see-saw – as long as they take it slow!

MILLY MONKEY

WILLY MONKEY

Slow down... don't bump me!

CORAL MONKEY

CALLIE UNICORN

See-saw slip-up
Gigi once launched off the see-saw when Marge sat down hard at the other end.

TWIRL-A-WHIRL

CAROUSEL

Abigail loves a spin on the Twirl-a-Whirl. She could hang on by her tail, but it's nice to buckle in and let the harness do the work.

LAYLA UNICORN

LILY UNICORN

ABIGAIL MONKEY

Heart start
A twist of the purple heart at the top sets the carousel spinning.

MEET THE MINIS!

The Minis are itty-bitty Fingerlings who just love to hang out together. They link their tails, arms or legs to form a chain – then they hook onto something and get swinging. There are really no limits to how many Minis can make up a chain. "The more the merrier" is their motto.

These tiny tearaways create lots of fun in Melody Village. They create lots of mischief, too. They may be small, but there are dozens of them and they always act as a team. When the Minis get together to play a prank, the bigger Fingerlings had better watch out!

ALIKA

AMELIA

ARCHIE

ARIANNA

BAMBOO

BEANIE

BELLA

BETTY

BLOSSOM

BORIS

BREE

CARLY

CLARA

CLEO

DELILAH

DEMI

DREW

ELSA

EMILY

ERIN

FAYE

GEMMA

GIGI

GOLDY

HARLEY

HARPER

HEIDI

JAMIE

JENNY

JOANA

JOELLE

JOY

JULES

KAIT

KARA

94

KAYLIN

KIKI

KINGSLEY

KYLIE

KYRIE

LANA

LEMONY

LIL' G

LISA

LIV

LOGAN

LOLA

MACKENZIE

MACY

MARA

MARGE

MEADOW

MEG

MEGAN

MELODY

MIA

MILO

MIMI

MOLLY

NAÏMA

NEVE

NOA

OLIVIA

OPAL

PEACH

PIPPA

POLLY

REESE

ROMY

ROSE

SANDY

SCOUT

SHELLY

SHIMMER

SHIRLEY

SKYE

SUGAR

TAMMY

TARA

TESS

TIA

TINY

TWINKLE

WINNIE

ZOE

Editorial Assistant Vicky Armstrong
Designer Stefan Georgiou
Pre-Production Producer Marc Staples
Producer Lloyd Robertson
Managing Editor Sarah Harland
Managing Art Editor Guy Harvey
Publisher Julie Ferris
Art Director Lisa Lanzarini
Publishing Director Simon Beecroft

Written by Julia March

Dorling Kindersley would like to thank Lori Hand
and Nicole Reynolds for editorial assistance.

First published in Great Britan in 2019 by
Dorling Kindersley Limited
80 Strand, London WC2R 0RL
A Penguin Random House Company

10 9 8 7 6 5 4 3 2 1
001–314516–Sept/2019

A CIP catalogue record for this book is available from the British Library.

ISBN: 978-0-24138-500-5

Printed and bound in China

www.fingerlings.com

A WORLD OF IDEAS:
SEE ALL THERE IS TO KNOW
www.dk.com